Advent Antics

An activity book for children

Katie Thompson

Illustrated by Arthur Baker

First published in 1999 by
KEVIN MAYHEW LTD
Buxhall
Stowmarket
Suffolk IP14 3DJ

0 1 2 3 4 5 6 7 8 9

ISBN 1 84003 393 2
Catalogue No 1500288

Edited by Katherine Laidler
Cover designed by Jonathan Stroulger
Illustrated by Arthur Baker
Typesetting by Richard Weaver
Printed and bound in Great Britain

Introduction

If you want a fun-filled countdown to Christmas, then this little book is for you!

Beginning on 1 December, the Christmas story unfolds day by day, with all sorts of antics for you to enjoy along the way. There is a different activity each day – picture and number puzzles, word games, quizzes, and codes to crack – with a special message waiting for you to discover on Christmas Day!

Have fun!

Zechariah the priest and his wife Elizabeth were good people who obeyed God. They had no children and as they grew older they realised, sadly, that a child of their own was impossible.

Then one day an angel called Gabriel appeared to Zechariah in the Temple, and told him that he and Elizabeth were going to have a son.

CODE CRACKER

△	A	Y	O	L
□	N	B	U	S
◇	J	C	H	R
	→	↓	←	↑

'

△↓ △← □←   □↑ ◇← △→ △↑ △↑

◇↓ △→ △↑ △↑   △↓ △← □← ◇↑

'

□↑ △← □→   ◇→ △← ◇← □→

Gabriel told Zechariah, 'Your son will be blessed by God.'

Zechariah could not believe his ears! 'Surely we are too old for this to happen!' he said.

Gabriel answered, 'God has sent me with this news for you! Because you have chosen to doubt my words, you will not be able to speak until everything happens as I have said.'

From that moment Zechariah could not speak, and, just as the angel had said, Elizabeth soon found that she was expecting a baby.

How many words can you make from these names?

ZECHARIAH	GABRIEL	ELIZABETH
chair	bag	the
hair	big	belt

3
December

God sent the angel Gabriel to a town in Galilee called Nazareth, to a young woman there called Mary. She was engaged to marry a carpenter called Joseph, a descendant of King David's family.

The angel greeted Mary with the words, 'Be glad, Mary, for God is with you and has given you great blessings.'

Mary was troubled and wondered what the angel's words could mean.

'There is nothing to fear,' Gabriel assured her. 'You will have a son and name him Jesus, and he will be called Son of the Most High, whose reign will never end.'

Can you spot ten differences in the bottom picture?

'How can this happen,' asked Mary, 'when I am not married?'

Gabriel answered, 'Nothing is impossible for God! The Holy Spirit will come to you and the power of God will cover you, so that this child will be holy and known as the Son of God. Even as we speak, your cousin Elizabeth, who was childless, is expecting a baby.'

Then Mary knelt before the angel and said to him . . .

Write the next letter of the alphabet on the lines above the letters given to read what Mary said!

A B C D E F G H I J K L M N O P Q R S T U V W X Y Z

‘ __ __ __ __ __ __ __ ,
  H   Z L   F N C R

__ __ __ __ __ __ __   __ __ __   __ __ __ __
R D Q U Z M S   Z M C   V H K K

__ __   __ __ __ __ __ __ __ __   __ __
C N   V G Z S D U D Q   G D

__ __ __ __ .
Z R J R

__ __ __   __ __ __ __ __ __ __ __ __ __
K D S   D U D Q X S G H M F

__ __ __ __ __ __   __ __ __ __   __ __
G Z O O D M   I T R S   Z R
                                          ,

__ __ __   __ __ __ __   __ __ __ __
X N T   G Z U D   R Z H C

After the angel's visit, Mary set off at once to her cousin's house in the hills of Judaea. As soon as Elizabeth heard Mary's greeting, she felt her unborn child leap for joy inside her. Filled with the Holy Spirit, Elizabeth knew at once that Mary had been chosen to be the mother of God's Son.

Mary stayed with her cousin for three months before returning home to Nazareth in Galilee.

Help Mary to find her way to Elizabeth's house

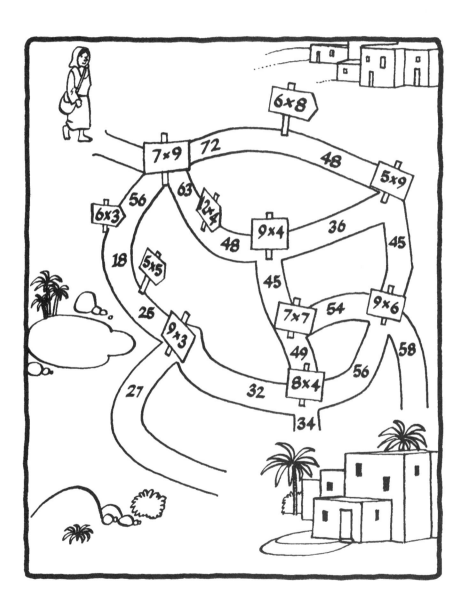

Soon after Mary had returned home,
Elizabeth gave birth to a son, just as the
angel had said. Zechariah and Elizabeth's
friends and relatives praised God, thanking
him for his goodness, and together they
celebrated the happy event.

When the baby was a week old, they took
him to the Temple, according to the Law.

Write the letter missing from the second word in the box to find out where the Temple was

In **JACKET** but not in **PACKET**

In **TEN** but not in **TIN**

In **BREAD** but not in **BEAD**

In **RUIN** but not in **RAIN**

In **STRAW** but not in **WATER**

In **SAW** but not in **SEW**

In **LADDER** but not in **ADDER**

In **SWEET** but not in **SWAT**

In **MAT** but not in **CAT**

7 December

The people in the Temple said, 'Surely they will call him Zechariah after his father.'

But Elizabeth spoke up and said, 'His name will be John!'

'But there is no one in your family with that name!' the people exclaimed, and they turned to Zechariah to ask for his opinion.

Zechariah still couldn't speak, but, remembering the angel's words, he carefully wrote, 'His name is John!'

At that moment his speech returned, and, filled with the Holy Spirit, he said, 'Praise the God of Israel, for you, my child, will be called a prophet of God. You will prepare a path for the Lord, telling his people that, through the forgiveness of their sins, they will be saved!'

Use the picture clues to fill in the crossword and see who this baby grew up to be!

8 December

Meanwhile Mary had told Joseph that she was expecting a baby. Joseph, who was a good and kind man, wanted to protect Mary from scandal, so he decided to break off their engagement quietly.

But one night, as Joseph slept, an angel appeared to him and said, 'Joseph, descendant of David, do not be afraid to take Mary as your wife, because this child has been conceived by the Holy Spirit. Mary will have a son and you will call him Jesus.'

When Joseph woke up, he did as the angel had said and continued to make plans for their wedding.

At that time the Emperor Caesar Augustus ordered a census to be taken. This required everyone to return to their family town to be registered and counted.

So Joseph and Mary left Nazareth in Galilee and returned to Bethlehem in Judaea, because Joseph was a descendant of King David, and therefore Bethlehem (where King David was born) was Joseph's family town.

Help Mary and Joseph
to find the best route to Bethlehem
by completing the directions below

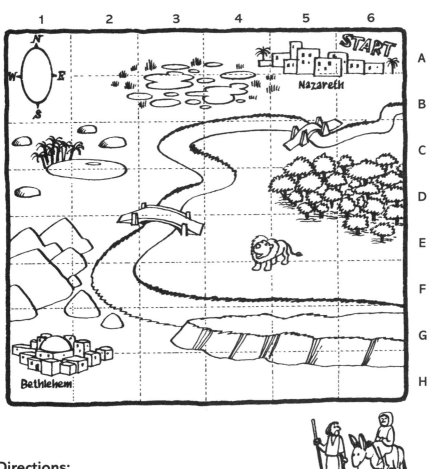

Directions:

6A, 6B, 5C

10

December

Mary, who was soon to have her baby, made the long journey, riding a little donkey led by Joseph.

Bethlehem was full of travellers, all arriving to register for the census. Everyone was looking for somewhere to stay and every inn was full. At each door they knocked on they were told the same thing: 'There's no room here, try somewhere else!'

Joseph grew more and more anxious because he knew that Mary's baby could be born at any time.

After a desperate search, they finally found a stable which was warm and dry, where they could shelter and rest.

Which inn has the most people staying there?

When the time came, Mary gave birth to a son and they called him Jesus, just as the angel had told them to.

They wrapped him snugly in strips of cloth, as was the custom, and gently laid him in a manger filled with fresh hay.

Safe and warm, the family slept peacefully while the animals in the stable watched over them.

Use the clues to find the name for the strips of cloth wrapped around baby Jesus

1.	2.	3.	4.	5.	6.	7.	8.	9.

1. Fifth letter of _ _ _ _ _ _ _

2. First letter of _ _ _ _ _ _

3. Third letter of _ _ _ _ _

4. Fourth letter of _ _ _ _

5. First letter of _ _ _ _

6. First letter of _ _ _ _ _ _

7. Second letter of _ _ _ _

8. Third letter of _ _ _ _ _ _ _

9. Third letter of _ _ _

12
December

On the hills near Bethlehem, some shepherds were keeping a sleepy watch over their sheep, when suddenly the night sky was ablaze with dazzling light, and an angel appeared before them.

The shepherds were terrified and hid their faces, but the angel reassured them, saying, 'Do not be afraid. I have come to give you good news, because tonight in Bethlehem your Saviour has been born. You will find the child sleeping in a manger there.'

Then the whole sky was filled with angels singing God's praise and wishing peace and joy to everyone. Never before had these simple shepherds heard such heavenly music or seen such a wondrous sight.

When the angels had left them, the shepherds were filled with wonder, and some of them hurried off to Bethlehem to see if they could find this very special child.

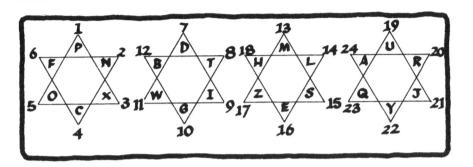

8 18 16 22   6 5 19 2 7
(THEY FOUND)

18 9 13   11 20 24 1 1 16 7
(HIM WRAPPED)

9 2   15 11 24 7 7 14 9 2 10
(IN SWADDLING)

4 14 5 8 18 16 15   24 2 7
(CLOTHES AND)

14 24 9 7   9 2   24
(LAID IN A)

13 24 2 10 16 20
(MANGER)

14
December

With great excitement, the shepherds began to tell Mary and Joseph about the marvellous things they had seen and heard that night, and about everything the angel had told them.

As the joyful shepherds left, singing songs of praise to God, Mary sat quietly with Jesus, wondering about everything the shepherds had said, and treasuring their words in her heart.

Help the shepherds to find their way through the streets of Bethlehem back to their sheep

15
December

About this time a bright new star appeared
in the night sky, and it was noticed far
away in the East by some wise men who
studied the heavens. Such a star caused
great excitement because, according to
their ancient writings, its appearance was a
sign that a new King of the Jews had been
born.

'He has probably been born in Jerusalem,'
they said, 'so we must visit him and bring
him gifts.'

Once preparations had been made, they
set off on their journey, determined to
follow the star wherever it led them.

Complete the crossword clues to find another name for someone who studies the stars and planets

1. First letter of the alphabet
2. Castles on the beach are made from this
3. An elephant's nose!
4. Water falling from clouds
5. The opposite of young
6. The best time to see the stars
7. The tenth month of the year
8. A 26-mile running race
9. The world's highest mountain
10. An arch of colours in the sky

1.	2.	3.	4.	5.	6.	7.	8.	9.	10.

_____ _____ _____ _____ _____

_____ _____ _____ _____ _____

_____ _____ _____ _____ _____

_____ _____ _____

_____ _____ _____

_____

Before long, news reached King Herod that some wise men from the East had arrived in Jerusalem and were searching for a newborn king. Herod was worried by this, so he sent for his advisers.

How many crowns can you find hidden in King Herod's throne room?

Crowns

17 December

King Herod asked his advisers, 'Tell me, have the prophets foretold of such a king?'

'Indeed, your majesty,' they replied. 'The prophet Micah tells us that a great leader will be born not far from here in Bethlehem.'

Now Herod was really worried! Another king would be a threat to his kingdom and power, so he began to plot and scheme to find a way to solve his problem.

Use the key to find the words of the prophet Micah

A	B	C	D	E	F	H	I	L	M	N	O	P	R	S	T	U	W	Y

18 December

King Herod invited the wise men to his palace. He asked them how much they knew about the newborn king, and wanted to know the exact time that the star had appeared.

'My advisers tell me that our prophets speak of a great leader being born at a place called Bethlehem,' Herod told his visitors helpfully. 'I want you to find him,' he said cunningly, 'so that I can go and pay my respects.'

This invitation has been accidentally torn! Can you piece it together for the wise men to read?

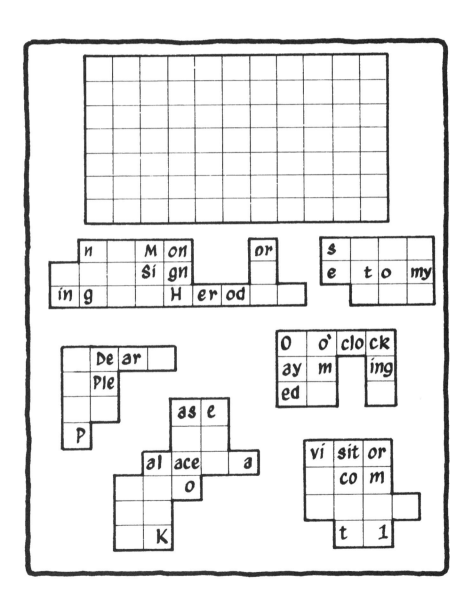

19
December

The wise men agreed to send news of the new king when they found him, because they knew nothing of Herod's wicked plan to kill his rival.

Then they thanked him for his kindness and set off to continue their quest without further delay. King Herod watched them go and waited anxiously for news.

20
December

The bright new star guided the wise men until they reached the town called Bethlehem. There it seemed to hang in the sky and shine even more brilliantly above the place where Jesus was.

After their long journey of discovery, the wise men were overjoyed to find, at last, the special child they had travelled so far to see.

Circle the objects which do not belong in this picture

The wise men knelt before Jesus and laid
their gifts at his feet as they worshipped
him – gold, frankincense and myrrh.

The wise men stayed a while and marvelled
at this wondrous child, pondering about
everything they had seen.

Which wise man brought which gift?

Herod waited impatiently for news from the foreign visitors about where he could find the newborn king who troubled him so much.

No message ever came, however, because the wise men were warned in a dream about Herod's wicked plans, and they took great care to return to their own country by a different route.

Use the directions to plot the wise men's route home

Ap, Bo, Cn, Bm, Cm, Dm, Em, Fm, Gl, Fk, Ek, Fj, Gi, Hi, Hj

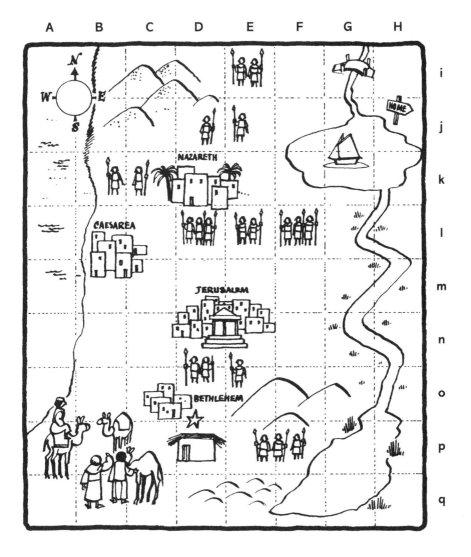

Soon after the wise men's visit, an angel
sent by God appeared to Joseph in a
dream and warned, 'Joseph, you and your
family are in great danger! You must take
Mary and Jesus, and flee to Egypt this very
night. Stay there until I tell you that it is
safe to return. King Herod intends to find
Jesus and kill him!'

So Joseph got up and they set off for
Egypt while it was still dark.

Can you find these words hidden in the wordsearch?

PERIL   JEOPARDY   RISK   HAZARD   FEAR

VULNERABLE   THREATENED   DANGER   TERROR

S	E	L	B	A	R	E	N	L	U	V
R	M	P	T	E	R	R	O	R	P	M
M	Y	B	L	S	P	R	F	E	A	R
V	D	K	H	A	Z	A	R	D	J	I
O	R	N	Q	X	A	I	E	P	R	S
T	A	P	L	F	L	L	X	E	W	K
B	P	J	U	A	S	W	G	S	I	N
G	O	Y	R	E	H	N	O	C	U	R
D	E	N	E	T	A	E	R	H	T	M
V	J	Z	T	D	K	Y	M	Z	Q	P

When King Herod realised that the wise men had tricked him, he flew into an uncontrollable rage. He summoned his soldiers and gave them his terrible orders.

As the soldiers carried out Herod's cruel command, Jesus and his family were already many miles away.

```
AB
GH   CD
EF
```

IJ	KL	MN
OP	QR	ST
UV	WX	YZ

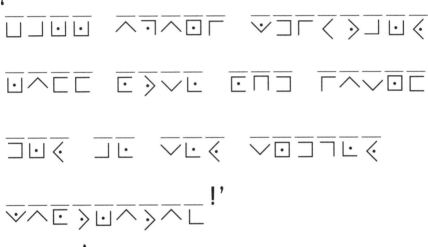

Some time later, when King Herod was dead, the angel returned to Joseph, just as he had promised, and told him that it was safe to return.

So Joseph and his family left Egypt. They returned to Galilee and went to live in Nazareth.

Moving clockwise around the circle, write down every other letter. Do this twice to find a Christmas message!

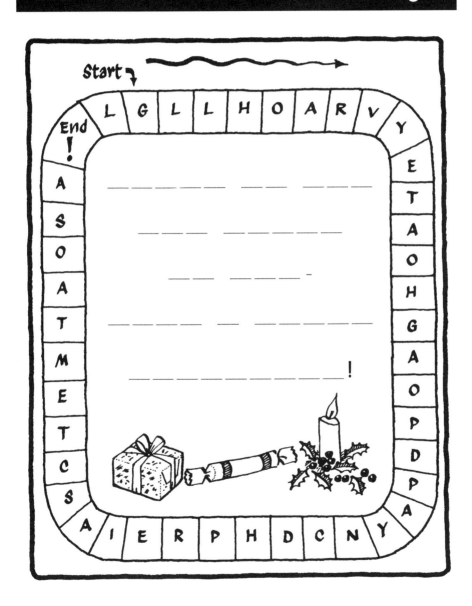